WALT DISNEY'S
Cinderella
SPECIAL EDITION

A DREAM COME TRUE

THE STORYBOOK AND THE
MAKING OF A MASTERPIECE

DISNEY
EDITIONS
NEW YORK

For information address:
Disney Editions
114 Fifth Avenue
New York, NY 10011-5690

Disney Editions Editorial Director: Wendy Lefkon
Disney Editions Editor: Jody Revenson

Produced by Welcome Enterprises, Inc.
6 West 18th Street, New York, NY 10011
www.welcomebooks.com

Written by Jim Fanning
Designed by Timothy Shaner
and H. Clark Wakabayashi

ISBN 0-7868-4940-1

Printed in Canada

Contents

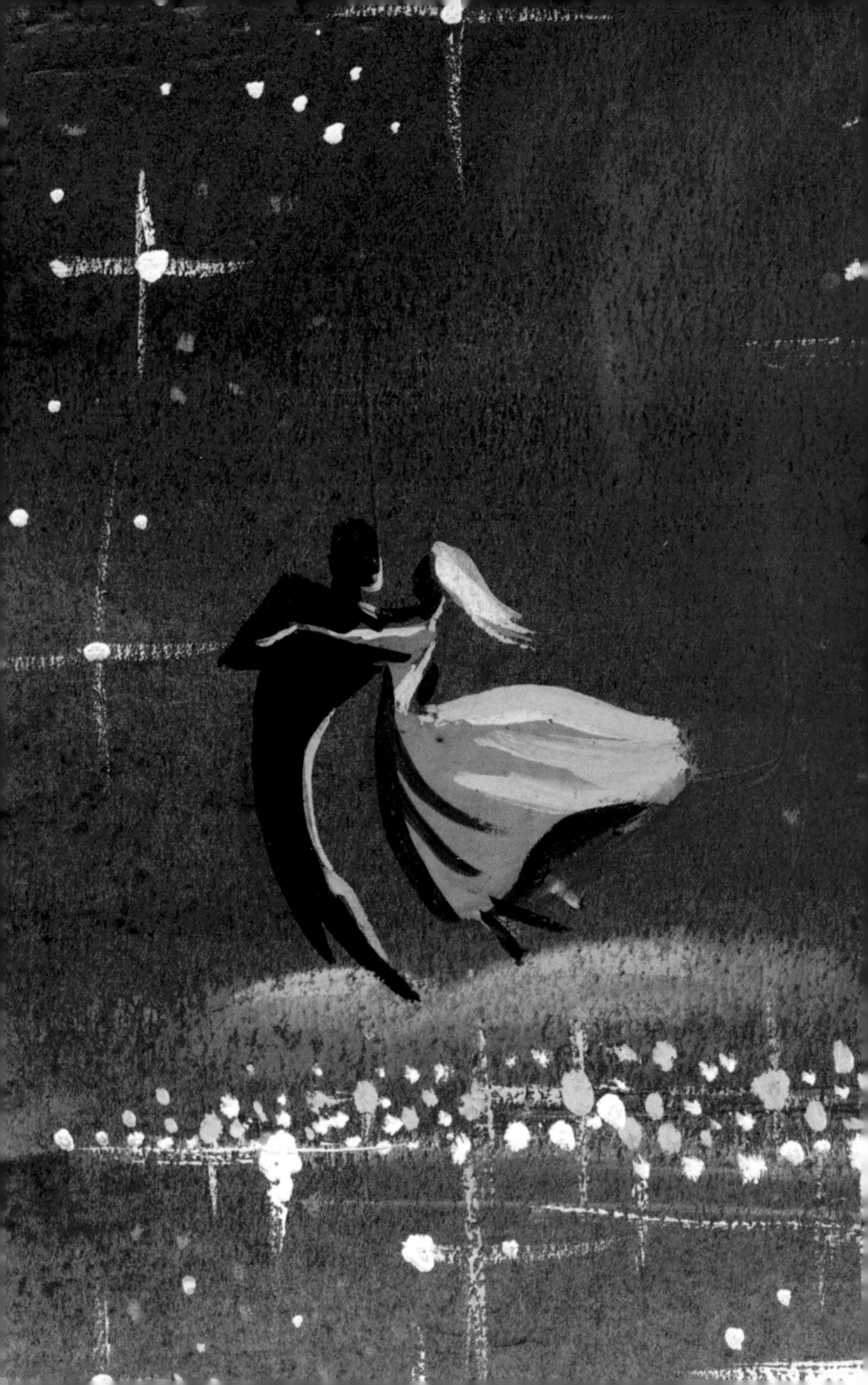

INTRODUCTION

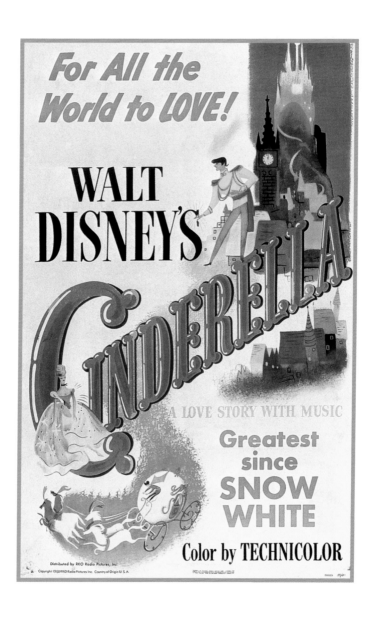

*O*f all Walt Disney's animated classics, none is more cherished than *Cinderella*. Based on the world's most beloved fairy tale, the magical, musical story of the beautiful scullery maid who goes from "rags to riches" with the help of her Fairy Godmother has been enthralling audiences for more than fifty years. And thanks to an extensive restoration effort, today's viewers can see a *Cinderella* that looks as beautiful as the day it premiered.

To create his first true animated feature in nearly a decade, Walt Disney employed moviemaking more magical than even Cinderella's Fairy

Godmother. An experienced team of more than 750 artists used over one million drawings, 1,500 glowing colors, and six unforgettable songs to conjure up an enchanting animated fantasy that has held the world spellbound ever since. Walt Disney's *Cinderella* triumphantly reestablished the animated feature as an art form and earned itself a treasured place of honor on the long list of Disney classics.

A masterwork of brilliant animation, spectacular effects, sparkling music, dynamic storytelling, and immortal characters, *Cinderella* was one of Walt Disney's favorite films and is an enchanting "dream come true" that will endure forever.

Opposite: Conceptual study.

THE STORYBOOK

ONCE UPON A TIME, in a faraway kingdom, there lived a lovely girl named Cinderella. Cinderella was as kind as she was beautiful.

Below: Preliminary character sketches.
Opposite: Conceptual study by stylist Mary Blair.
Previous pages: Background painting.

13

But her wicked stepmother and her selfish stepsisters were jealous of Cinderella's gentle grace, and they forced her to become a servant in her own home. Day after day, Cinderella slaved away doing all the work . . . but she never gave up her dreams.

Above: Early character study.

One day, an invitation
was issued to every maiden
in the kingdom. A Royal
Ball was to be held in
honor of his highness,
Prince Charming.

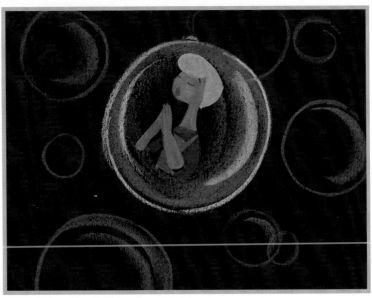

inderella knew she was invited to the ball, too, and her stepmother said she could go if she had a proper dress.

inderella began to make a dress for herself. But her stepsisters selfishly kept her so busy that Cinderella had no time to work on the dress. So Cinderella's loyal friends, the bluebirds and the little mice, finished the dress for her.

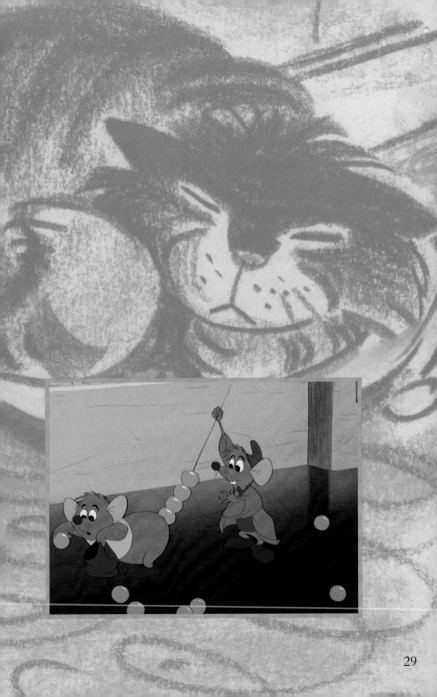

Right: Early conceptual painting.

32

But the jealous stepsisters cruelly ripped Cinderella's dress apart and departed for the ball. Heartbroken, Cinderella ran crying into the garden.

Suddenly, Cinderella's Fairy
Godmother magically appeared.
With a wave of her wand and
saying the magic words . . .

"Bibbidi-Bobbidi-Boo,"

the Fairy Godmother turned
a pumpkin into a fine glowing
coach, and the mice into
magnificent horses . . .

. . . and Cinderella's rags
into a shimmering gown,
complete with glass slippers.

Animation drawing
by Marc Davis with
effect overlay.

41

Remember," warned the Fairy Godmother as Cinderella left for the ball, "the spell will be broken at midnight."

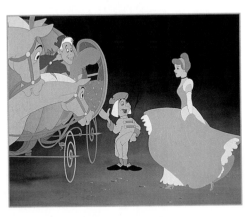

Right: Conceptual study.

At the ball, Cinderella was by far the loveliest lady there. Prince Charming danced with Cinderella, and they fell in love.

The first stroke of mid-
night reminded Cinderella
of her Fairy Godmother's
words. She hurried down
the palace steps and lost
one of her glass slippers.

63

As she rode away
in her magical coach, the
spell was broken . . . and
everything was as before.

ut the Prince could
not forget the beautiful girl.
He promised to marry
whoever could fit the glass
slipper. The Grand Duke
went from house to house,
trying the shoe on every
girl in the land.

At last he came to the chateau where Cinderella lived . . . where her heartless stepmother had locked Cinderella in her tower room. The brave mice Jaq and Gus knew it was up to them to rescue Cinderella. They got the key from the stepmother's pocket and carried it up the long staircase.

Above: Conceptual study.

Cinderella hurried downstairs just as the Duke was about to leave.

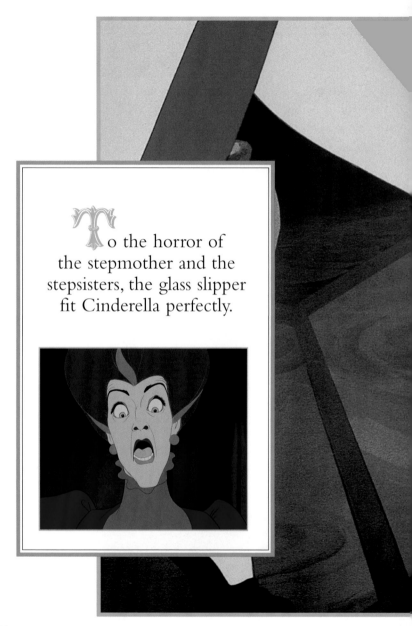

To the horror of
the stepmother and the
stepsisters, the glass slipper
fit Cinderella perfectly.

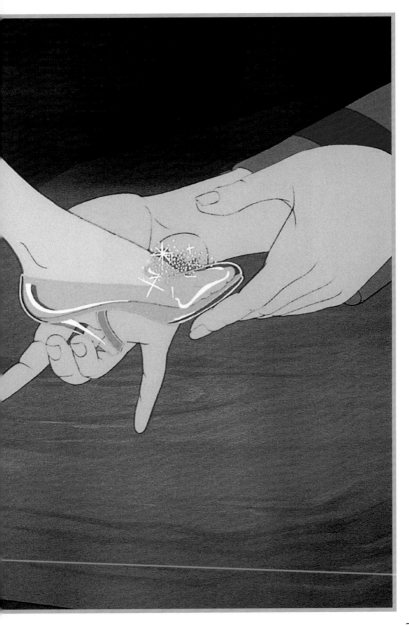

To the joy of her
animal friends, Cinderella
and the Prince were married
and lived . . .

Happily ever after.

The Making of
a Masterpiece

ORIGINAL STORY

inderella is the most classic of all love stories," observed Disney animator Marc Davis. "It's the one story that practically everyone in the world knows." The quintessential fairy story, the Cinderella legend has been found in the folklore of ancient Egypt, Rome,

Opposite: Study for ballroom sequence.

and among tales told by Native American tribes. The downtrodden heroine and her hope of finding a prince or chief of great charm and wealth is the common link among all the variations of the fable.

The story we know specifically as "Cinderella" is mentioned in 16th-century German literature. Poet Charles Perrault popularized the story in his 1697 collection of folk tales, and it is this French version that Walt Disney chose as the basis for his film.

John Hench, a stylist/designer on *Cinderella*, commented that fairy tales "all fall into a pattern, often a Biblical pattern. In the case of Cinderella, she was very high-born [and] was reduced to a kitchen maid. This is clearly Man

being kicked out of Eden. Along comes
a redeemer, a prince, and there's always
a gimmick, a key, a talisman. . . . In
Cinderella it's a glass slipper. And the
person is returned to the former state."
Whatever the details through the
centuries, the basic truth of the
Cinderella story remains: virtue is more
important than riches, and goodness
will always be rewarded.

Right: The ornate storybook used
in the film's opening sequence.
Below: Promotional art.

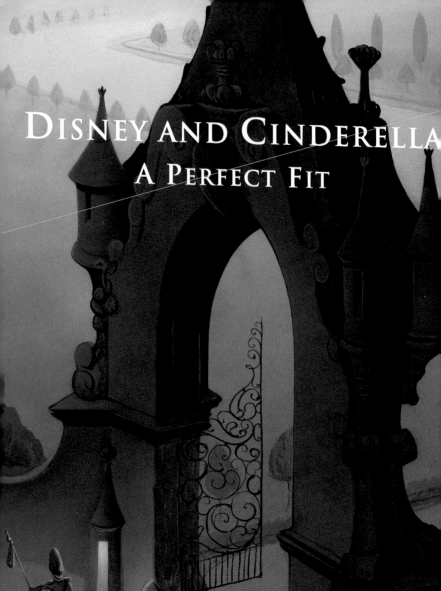

DISNEY AND CINDERELLA
A PERFECT FIT

Above: Walt Disney studies a piece of
conceptual art. Left: An early story sketch
includes one of the many names considered for Cinderella's mouse friends.

DUSTY   POPS   OUT—
(2-12-40)

(By Dora Coty

Right: Story sketch of Cinderella
being awakened by bluebirds.

Walt Disney had not made a true animated feature since *Bambi* (1942). The "package pictures" such as *Make Mine Music* (1946) and *Melody Time* (1948) attracted little attention at the box office. "Walt had gone so long without a hit, and he was really in debt," Disney animator Frank Thomas said. Disney recognized that the only way to reclaim commercial success—and to give his accomplished artists an opportunity to shine—

"Walt finally decided the one thing audiences respond to is a girl in trouble."

—FRANK THOMAS

Preliminary pencil sketch depicting
first appearance of the Fairy Godmother.

was to produce a full-length, single-story animated feature.

But *what* feature? *Cinderella* had been in development for some years. Disney's first attempt at telling the *Cinderella* story was in a 1922 short produced in Kansas City as part of Walt's silent "Laugh-O-Grams" animated series. The story was considered for possible production as a *Silly Symphony* short in 1933, and a complete set of feature-length storyboards was produced as early as 1940. But other projects were in the works, too, such as *Peter Pan* and

Alice in Wonderland. At last, Walt decided that *Cinderella* had the same strengths as his first feature triumph, *Snow White and the Seven Dwarfs* (1937).

The Disney artists were thrilled with Walt's choice. "Everyone was delighted to get back to work on something that was important," remembered animator Milt Kahl. The challenge for Disney and his staff was retelling the well-known fairy story through animation, making the age-old tale fresh and new. Disney and his story team used Perrault's original as a basic structure and began

developing human and animal characters to add the Disney touch. At one point, Disney even considered bringing back Snow White and her animal friends in this new story.

As he had with *Snow White*, Walt Disney was risking everything—his financial resources, his reputation, and his very future—on an animated fairy tale. If *Cinderella* was not the magical masterpiece he envisioned, it would spell the end of the Disney Studios.

CINDERELLA
EVER GENTLE AND KIND

From the start, Walt Disney knew the creation of a touching, involving feature would rest on the lovely shoulders of his leading lady. "I think the picture has to play from Cinderella's standpoint," he told his artists at a 1946 story meeting. "You will laugh and cry for her—and pull for her."

Above: Stylists John Hench and Mary Blair, Walt Disney, and background artist Claude Coats discuss background paintings.

To create a sympathetic Cinderella, Disney assigned a team of his top artists, including veteran animator Marc Davis. As assistant to animator Grim Natwick, Davis had helped bring the little princess of Disney's landmark first feature, *Snow White and the Seven Dwarfs*, to life; now Disney relied on Davis to give beauty and grace to another fairy tale princess. "I didn't come to the Studio expecting to do female characters," recalled Davis, "but because of my early work with Grim Natwick

on *Snow White*, I ended up doing several of them. I worked in story on *Cinderella* so I think it was just accepted I would do the girl."

Davis was well aware of the importance of creating a convincing heroine. "Cinderella carries the story," he observed. "If you don't believe in her, it doesn't matter how good or funny or interesting the rest of the characters are—the picture just doesn't work. With Cinderella, you could see the hurt and see the feeling. But even though she had

Opposite and below: Character studies by Marc Davis.

her sad moments, she still stood rather strong all the way through. The audience had to believe she was worth their concern."

Though the design of *Cinderella* evolved during the years the film was in development, it took Davis and the other artists assigned to the character an intense period of four months to create the final version. Even the color of her hair was determined only after extensive research and experimentation.

Eighteen-year-old redheaded actress Helene Stanley was instrumental in creating the animated performance of Cinderella. Stanley mimed the role of the lovely scullery maid for the live-action camera under the direction of the artists. Working with enlarged photo-

stats of Stanley's performances, the animators interpreted and redesigned the poses to meet the needs of animated acting and storytelling. Eric Larson, another leading animator who gave life to the fairy tale's leading lady, noted Stanley's contribution, stating that she had an "appreciation of what animation was all about. She understood the medium like few people did and

Above: Helene Stanley reviews storyboards during filming.

was a great inspiration to the animators in creating a convincingly lifelike girl."

To create the beautiful young woman whose kindness wins out over oppression and cruelty, Walt Disney told his animators, "I want to be hit right here in the heart." With a lot of hard work and constant effort behind the scenes, Cinderella does just that for whoever sees her on screen. If Snow White is the first lady of animation, Cinderella is surely the crown princess.

Cinderella's Voice

The expressive singing and speaking voice of Cinderella was cast almost by accident. Songwriters Mack David, Jerry Livingston, and Al Hoffman had written their first *Cinderella* song, "A Dream Is A Wish Your Heart Makes."

"When we went to play it for Walt he simply said, 'That'll work,' and asked us to have a demo record

Below: Early costume study for ball gown. Right: Early cel study of Cinderella.

made," Livingston remembered. " We weren't sure who to use for the vocal since we were new to Hollywood. Finally, Mack remembered that Ilene Woods, a singer we knew from the *Hit Parade*, was now living in Hollywood, so we used her. When Walt heard her voice,

he got excited. . . . The next thing we knew, she was hired for the voice of Cinderella."

Woods, a popular radio singer, recalled that "I had done the recording not as an audition but as a favor to Mack and Jerry. I was totally surprised when I got a call

Above: Ilene Woods.

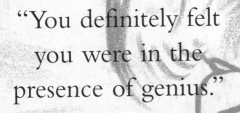

"You definitely felt
you were in the
presence of genius."

—ILENE WOODS

several days later saying Walt Disney wanted to meet me." Three hundred fifty actresses had already auditioned, but when Disney heard Woods's reading he immediately knew he had found his Cinderella. "I was the first non-soprano the Studio ever hired," she said. "Walt would come in towards the end of each recording session and suggest different ways of doing things. There was a real aura about him. You definitely felt that you were in the presence of genius."

When she finally saw the completed *Cinderella* at the premiere, long after she recorded her vocal performance, Woods was so caught up in the film that she forgot she had anything to do with it.

Her parents recognized some of their daughter's facial expressions,

such as squinting her eyes, that the animators had incorporated into the character. Years later, when Woods's young daughter saw the film, the three-and-a-half-year-old stood up in the theater and shouted, "that's my mommy!"

THE STEPMOTHER
PORTRAIT OF EVIL

Even without the black magic of the evil Queen or Maleficent, or the flamboyance of Cruella De Vil, Cinderella's wicked stepmother stands as one of Disney's most frightening villains on the strength of her subtle but powerful cruelty. Walt Disney described the stepmother, one of the most famous of fairy tale evildoers, as having "a certain cruel dignity." To bring the power that description implies to animated life, Disney cast Frank Thomas as the wicked woman's directing animator. "I knew Walt was going to make *Cinderella* but I didn't know I was going to do the stepmother," remembered

Thomas. "It seemed like such a heavy assignment, I didn't know who could handle it. 'Boy,' I thought, 'that's a tough assignment for some poor guy. I wonder who's going to get it?'"

"The stepmother was one of the toughest characters I did," Thomas revealed. "I felt that for the story to work, the stepmother had to be as realistic as Cinderella herself. She couldn't be as cartoony or buffoonish as the King or the Grand Duke or the stepsisters. I had to find ways to draw her not realistically, but as convincingly as Cinderella was drawn. The drawing itself was so meticulous, and with

Opposite: Eleanor Audley, the voice of the stepmother, acts out the role for the animators' reference.

110

"Boy," I thought, "that's a tough assignment for some poor guy. I wonder who's going to get it?"

—FRANK THOMAS

Marc Davis and Eric Larson working on Cinderella, it was a tough standard to try to come up to."

For inspiration, Thomas turned to live-action reference film of Eleanor Audley, the veteran character actress who was also the voice of the stepmother. "Eleanor was excellent to work with, very understanding of the picture and its needs," Thomas observed, "and how the stepmother should behave and what her emotional attitudes should be. I would have been lost without Eleanor's live action to give me a role model, even though the

stepmother's design was quite different in proportion from Eleanor or any real person."

"There was some awfully good work in the story there, too, probably from Walt," added Thomas. "In the scene where the stepmother has the stepsisters tear poor Cinderella's gown

all to pieces, she says, 'Now come
along, girls, I won't have you upsetting
yourselves.' Gee, what a cold, icy
attitude—and what a great thing to
animate to. Quite a challenge—it
was all in her eyes, in her mouth, in her
posture. Boy, that was a tough one!"

LUCIFER

Every hero needs a villain, and while Cinderella had the stepmother, Gus and Jaq contended with the nasty, spoiled feline, Lucifer. Walt Disney described the lazy tabby as a "comic heavy."

"When the stepmother calls Cinderella in," Disney elaborated, "she sits with the cat, and the cat is looking up at Cinderella and just loving all the stuff the stepmother is pouring on Cinderella. You'll hate him. The animals all hate him."

"Walt always thought cats were villains," said Ward Kimball, directing animator on Lucifer. "I was having trouble designing that sinister-looking cat. Our family had a cat with seven toes. When Walt came out one day, he saw our cat and he said, 'There's your model for Lucifer.'" The fat, furry calico became the basis for the comically villainous cat you love to hate.

THE STEPSISTERS

Cinderella's mean stepsisters bring both comedy and menace to Disney's version of the famed fairy story. "You have to have all the live-action characters believable," noted Ollie Johnston, the directing animator behind Anastasia and Drizella. The caricatured design of the stepsisters works effectively with the more realistic look of Cinderella and the stepmother, the result of careful planning and keen artistic observation. "I couldn't go so far out with the stepsisters that they couldn't conceivably be the daughters of

Above: Live-action reference film still.

120

"The two sisters are
a couple of spoiled brats."

—*WALT DISNEY*

the stepmother. I had a closeup of
Anastasia that Walt felt was a little too
ugly in her smile so he asked me to
correct it. Walt didn't like ugliness. He
wanted even his villains to have appeal,
so I toned the stepsisters down to the
point where you could accept them.
You had to dislike them, but you didn't
have to be revolted by them."

The entertaining and effective
voices of the stepsisters were per-
formed by Rhoda Williams (Drizella)
and Lucille Bliss (Anastasia). Bliss,
who went on to be one of TV

ANASTASIA

DRIZEL
SAME
AS

122

animation's busiest voice talents (she was Smurfette on *The Smurfs*), was cast by Walt Disney himself after Bliss' improvisational audition for all the female parts in *Cinderella*.

"The two sisters are a couple of spoiled brats," was how Walt Disney summed up the characters, "a couple of sow's ears [that the stepmother] is trying to turn into silk purses."

Opposite background: Model sheet detail.

THE FAIRY
GODMOTHER

The Fairy Godmother has a brief but pivotal and all-important role, miraculously making it possible for Cinderella to attend the Royal Ball. But unlike the Perrault original in which the Godmother was an old crone, Walt Disney envisioned the magical being as a lovably comical character. "I don't see her as goofy or stupid, but rather as having a wonderful sense of humor," Disney said. Milt Kahl, who animated the Fairy Godmother, summed up her jovial personality by saying, "She is a good-natured

person [who] would laugh at the drop of a hat."

"[The Fairy Godmother] should have a kindly voice with a certain age in it," said Walt Disney, and Verna Felton provided the proper grandmotherly tones for the Godmother. As the enchantress who helps Cinderella's dreams come true, Felton particularly shone in her delightful performance of the jaunty "Bibbidi-Bobbidi-Boo." One of Disney's favorite voice talents, Felton also gave voice to the matriarch elephant in *Dumbo* (1941), the Queen of Hearts in *Alice in Wonderland* (1951), Aunt Sarah in *Lady and the Tramp* (1955), and another good fairy, Flora in *Sleeping Beauty* (1959).

FAIRY GODMOTHER

Left: Model sheet detail.

"The Fairy Godmother
should have a kindly voice
with a certain age in it."

—*Walt Disney*

THE MICE

"We can do it!
We can help our Cinderelly."

As with *Snow White and the Seven Dwarfs*, Walt Disney created lovable comedic characters to support his fairy tale heroine. But unlike *Snow White*, where the Dwarfs were already integral to the story, Disney had to start from scratch for *Cinderella*. "We have to build up Cinderella's little friends," Walt directed. "Pick animals that could be closer to her. She [needs] someone sympathetic to talk to." A flock of delightful bluebirds, the faithful old steed Major, and the loyal dog Bruno were developed, but it was the mice, particularly Jaq

Right: Story sketch.

129

and Gus, who came to the film's
forefront as Cinderella's companions.
Disney laughed upon seeing the first
animation of Jaq and Gus. "Marvelous,"
he told animator Ward Kimball. "Those
are funny characters."

"I was in charge of the mice,"
recalled Kimball. "That was a lot of fun
because it was the first time we based a
character on a caricature of the real
thing. We tried to give
the mice little
pointed noses with
whiskers and
mouse ears, and
that was quite a
breakthrough,
especially after
years of drawing

a mouse like Mickey. It pointed up the value of caricaturing the real thing."

Though mice are only mentioned in the Perrault original as the animals the Fairy Godmother transforms into horses to pull Cinderella's pumpkin coach, Disney considered the new personalities as enhancement of the classic story. He later said that "to some [timeless] stories a film version can give wider scope and even add characters without damage to the original tale. In *Cinderella* . . . there was every proof that audiences enjoyed our addition of the mice characters, Gus and Jaq, and the

valiant, fun-loving little band of
Cinderella's helpers."

The resourceful band of critters
have the little-known names of Luke
(the smallest), Mert and Bert (the
twins), and Suzy, Blossom, and Perla (the
women). But it was clever Jaq and dim-
witted Gus who teamed up as the true
stars of the mice set. *Newsweek* stated
that with Jaq and Gus, "Disney has a
pair of heroes the like of which has not
been seen since the reign of Mickey."

MOUSE LATIN

W hat's the feeling on the mice
talking?" asked Walt Disney at a story
conference. "We might want to
give them voices. It might be very

cute . . . when they are working that they have little songs they can sing." It was eventually decided that the mice would speak in a speeded-up, almost unintelligible version of English all their own, dubbed "Mouse Latin" by story-man Winston Hibler. "The audience will get a kick out of this, trying to figure it out," commented Disney. "Little cues like Cinderella's dialogue to the mice and their answers will help to carry it."

Disney's sound effects expert, Jimmy Macdonald, created the voices for the two main mice, Gus and Jaq, by speeding up the dialogue he recorded. Macdonald's expertise in sound wasn't the only reason he was the perfect choice to voice Cinderella's heroic

friends; he was also the voice of Mickey Mouse himself, taking over that role in 1947 when Walt Disney became too busy to perform the famous falsetto.

The delightfully high-pitched voices of Gus, Jaq, and the other mice are at their most endearing in "The Work Song."

"Walt had in mind some type of ballet sound for the music," said songwriter Jerry Livingston. "But after we discussed the action of the animals scurrying about, we knew we needed something light, yet frantic."

THE MUSIC

For his *Cinderella* songs, Walt Disney sought a special magical quality, and for the first time engaged composers outside his staff to create songs for an entire feature. Turning to New York's famed Tin Pan Alley, Disney was interested in the songwriting team of Mack David, Jerry Livingston, and Al Hoffman, who had crafted the popular novelty song "Mairzy Doats." Jerry Livingston remembered that on a trip to New York in 1947, Walt heard the trio's catchy hit

Above: Songwriters Mack David, Jerry Livingston, and Al Hoffman.

Walt wanted
the tunes to be
"story songs."

"Chi-Baba, Chi-Baba" and invited the songwriters to audition. "We played a medley of our songs for Walt," said Livingston, "but you could see that he was more interested in 'Chi-Baba.' I think then he had in mind something similar for the Fairy Godmother's magic scene. But he didn't want something ordinary like 'Ali Kazam.'" Disney liked the trio's playful but romantic style, and they headed for Hollywood where they spent the next nine months composing the *Cinderella* songs.

David, Livingston, and Hoffman found writing songs for Disney

Above: Original sheet music.

animation a unique assignment as Walt wanted the tunes to be "story songs." "In a live-action picture the story is sustained primarily by dialogue, and the song is mostly a pleasant interlude or an excuse to show off the vocal talents of the star," Mack David explained. "In a Disney picture the song must contribute to the story motif. Lyrics of the song must stem from the story and lead or flow back into the story. The lyrics often replace the dialogue so that if you were to eliminate any song from *Cinderella*, you  would probably have to cut 15 minutes from the story sequence as it would be

a definite interruption of the story line."

The Tin Pan Alley tunesmiths—who also wrote "The Unbirthday Song" for *Alice in Wonderland*—found the animation process fascinating and had great admiration for the Disney artists. "We thought our job was hard until we found out that it takes 10,000 drawings to make up seven minutes of animation," marvelled David. "We used to figure writing songs was exhausting. Then we decided we shouldn't complain; we had it easy."

The Disney animators in turn enjoyed working with the songwriters. "They were real nice guys, and their songs were just right for the picture," recalled animator Marc Davis. "Al, Jerry, and Mack were always together so we called them Manny, Moe, and Mack."

143

THE FINISHING TOUCHES:
FROM RAGS TO RICHES

GLASS SLIPPER

Layout artist Ken O'Connor was responsible for the design of Cinderella's sparkling glass slippers. "I bought some perfume bottles with exotic shapes," O'Connor explained. "I learned from them how to render glass in unusual shapes, such as a slipper. Then I could apply my knowledge of how the smooth glass catches light and reflects back sharp-edged highlights."

Ironically, the slippers in the fairy story were originally made of fur, but the French words for "glass" (verre) and "fur" (vair) are so close that a mistake was made in chronicling the

ancient tale, giving *Cinderella* one of its most unique elements.

PUMPKIN COACH

Walt Disney devoted particular attention to the Fairy Godmother's "Bibbidi-Bobbidi-Boo" sequence. "The carriage should be dainty," Walt said in describing the enchanted coach that started as a commonplace pumpkin. "The wheels shouldn't be enough to hold the weight. We should feel that it's a fairy carriage."

Cinderella layout artist Ken O'Connor was also charged with designing the pumpkin coach as fanciful but believable. "I built a three-dimensional model of the coach to ensure it worked with my layouts from all angles. I decided I'd make everything on the coach based on the pumpkin itself—wheels were tendrils spiraling out from the pumpkin which formed the body of the coach. A bud became a lantern and a leaf was the seat for the coachman. I showed Walt the coach model in fear and trembling

Opposite: Ilene Woods holds a model of the pumpkin coach.

because he was a sharp critic and
was usually right, too," O'Connor
remembered. "But he liked the model
right away. In fact he only asked me
one question, about how I soldered
the spokes to the rim of the wheel."

SHIMMERING BALL GOWN

The scene in which the Fairy Godmother fashions Cinderella's shimmering
ball gown had a special place in Walt
Disney's heart. Marc Davis, who
animated that magically memorable

Above: Animation drawings by Marc Davis.

148

moment, recalled that somebody asked
Walt, "'Of all the animation that has
been done at your studio, what is your
favorite?' Walt thought for a moment
and said, 'Well, I guess it would have
to be where Cinderella got her gown.'

"This is the magic of Walt Disney,
this tremendous optimist who really
believed that if you do things right,
somehow or other everything's going
to turn out right for you."

This enchanting piece of animated

magic helped make *Cinderella* one of Walt Disney's favorite films.

LIVE ACTION

In the earlier features, several scenes had been acted out with live actors in front of a camera as an aid to the animators. For *Cinderella*, all the sequences with human characters would be shot in live action first, so camera angles and staging decisions could be made before the costly process of animation was begun. Rudimentary sets served as backgrounds for models to silently act out the story to the prerecorded vocal track. In the scenes where Cinderella interacted

with the animals, tiny wire models were used to suggest mice or birds. "What Walt was trying to do was to make a picture where the animator and the director and the layout artist and everybody knew exactly what was being done," revealed Ollie Johnston. "With live action there was no mistake."

According to Marc Davis, "Cinderella's movements were never tracings of the live model because if you trace a photographic image with a flat line, the image becomes wide and gross. Live action is useful as a pattern to help you in the difficult things that you can't pull out of your head."

Above: Live-action reference still of Helene Stanley.
Opposite: Helene Stanley models the magical gown.

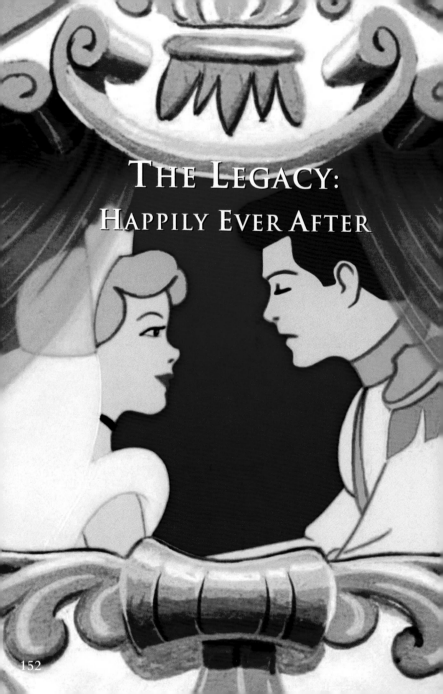

THE LEGACY:
HAPPILY EVER AFTER

Walt Disney attended every story meeting, developing characters, acting out bits of business, and creating key scenes and sequences directly from his imagination. As early as a major story conference on January 15, 1948, the entire film existed, scene by scene, in Walt's mind. The characters and

Above: *(back row)* Unidentified cameraman, story artist Winston Hibler, Helene Stanley; *(front row)* Director Wilfred Jackson, animator Milt Kahl, layout artist Ken O'Connor.

situations at this story meeting were essentially the version of *Cinderella* that would reach the screen in 1950.

After six years of effort and more than two million dollars, Walt Disney unveiled *Cinderella* on February 15,

1950. *Newsweek* celebrated the new classic with a cover story proclaiming, "*Cinderella* is a delightful carousel of humor, fantasy, and song . . . the finest Disney has ever achieved." Lines began forming at theaters the day the film opened. *Cinderella* was a smash box office hit, becoming one of the top movies of the year.

The first Disney tunes to be pub-
lished by the newly formed Walt Disney
Music Company, the *Cinderella* songs
were at the top of the charts, both as
recordings and sheet music. The motion
picture industry honored *Cinderella* with
three Academy Award® nominations—
for Best Score, Best Song ("Bibbidi-

Above: This conceptual painting helped establish the
romantic atmosphere of the Royal Ballroom.

Bobbidi-Boo"), and Best Sound.

The monumental success of Disney's new masterpiece put the Studio back on sound financial footing. "*Cinderella* saved the day," stated Frank Thomas. "We had our audience back and were back in the feature business." *Cinderella* reestablished Walt Disney's preeminence in the art form he had perfected. The artistic, critical, and box office success of *Cinderella* made possible Disneyland and the animated features that followed.

One of the most beloved of the Disney masterworks, *Cinderella* is second only to *Snow White and the Seven Dwarfs* in its timeless appeal. As a unique tribute to the Disney film that has touched hearts for generations, the 180-foot Cinderella Castle was made the landmark of the

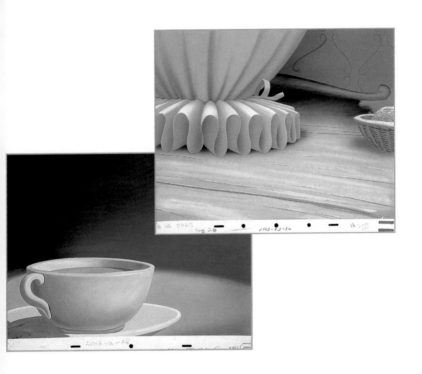

Magic Kingdom at Walt Disney World
Resort.

"*Cinderella* has magic in it,"
commented Marc Davis, "and it's all
good magic. In most fairy stories, the
magic is always evil. This is a story
where magic is for good. So I think this
is why *Cinderella* is *the* classic."

Above: Background paintings.

SPECIAL
ACKNOWLEDGMENT

To all the animators whose
loving dedication to their craft
helped transform the world's
most beloved fairy tale into a
timeless movie masterpiece.
And most of all, thank you,
Walt Disney, for your
inspiration, and for making so
many dreams come true.